THE GODS
OF THE ANCIENT GREEKS

Text by
Stella Kalogeraki
Archaeologist

Sketch
Gabriela Brioschi

Layout
Vangelis Papiomytoglou

Translation
Jill Pittinger

© Copyright
MEDITERRANEO EDITIONS
36 Govatzidaki str.
74100 Rethymno
tel. +30 28310 21590, fax +30 28310 21591
info@mediterraneo.gr
www.mediterraneo.gr

ISBN: 978-960-6848-15-5

THE GODS
OF THE ANCIENT GREEKS

THE FIRST GODS

Big bang, bam, boom! The noise must have been deafening. But nobody heard it, because nobody - and nothing - existed then! After that? There was…Chaos. Yes, that was created first of all – Chaos, and in it Eros and Gaia (Earth).

This is how Hesiod, a farmer from Boeotia who had the gift of poetry, imagined the creation of the world. But his undisciplined mind was unable to stop there.

"So - Chaos was created, Gaia (Earth) and Eros (Love). What about the rest? What about the gods? Who gave birth to the gods?"

He thought and thought over again. He really put his mind to it, saying that the story went on…

Besides, there was Eros, which made the situation easier. Eros generated life…

"I'll deal first of all with the subject of light," mused the poet, "because at present I don't even know where it…dawned!"

Here's a good idea: Chaos produced Night and Erebos. Then, because we can't always have black midnight, from the two of them there 'sprang' Day and Aethera. When the wind blew and light bathed Gaia (Earth), she seemed to be very…empty. Then she began to breed, so as not to be alone and miserable. Her first children – her pride and joy forever – were Uranos (Sky), Vouna (the Mountains), and Thalassa (the Sea). However, Earth wanted company. Sad as she was, she sat down on a little rock to think. Noticing the vastness of Uranos, she smiled at him. All at once, he answered. You see, he too was very lonely. Finally, the two not only became companions but produced a number of children. And not only just any, but big, healthy giants and cyclopes, as we call them. Yes, of course these kids had their little faults, but what can you say? Some had only one eye, others a hundred arms; the first were called 'Cyclopes', and the others 'Hundred Armed Ones'. Sheer terror! However, they also produced the twelve Titans – six boys and six girls – a feast for the eyes. Uranos was terrified – here monsters, there colossi. "Once they get it into their heads to take my throne, things will be difficult for me," he thought, and so he began to lock up his children deep inside the earth. When she heard about this, their mother got furious. She went and found her son, the Titan Kronos.

"Your father has gone crazy. Therefore, we must exterminate him. If you help me, I promise you his throne will be yours."

Kronos' eyes glistened and before you could

say 'jiminy' he had exterminated his father. Earth, who was delighted, made him king right away. Then he immediately released his Titan brothers and sisters. The others – the Cyclopes and the Hundred Armed Ones – he left down in the inky blackness. How's that for a brother! Oh well! The new king settled comfortably on his throne and began to review his kingdom. Under his rule he had the Earth, the mountains, the sea and his Titan siblings. He knitted his brows and muttered into his beard.

"Is this a kingdom or a mockery? We shall have to increase our numbers so that I have something to keep me busy."

He decided, therefore, to get married. Unfortunately there were no other prospective candidates for a bride for him to choose from, so he married his sister, the Titan Rhea. The other Titans did the same thing, and the world began to fill with children. Of course, the best of them - without argument - were those of Kronos and Rhea. These two produced the first and senior gods, Zeus, Poseidon, Hades, Hera, Demeter and Hestia. Isn't that something to brag about? Kronos shone with joy - until a little bug entered his brain.

"Could these kids of mine take away my throne?"

He didn't stop to think it over, but started to swallow them one by one, as soon as they were born. Rhea went mad. When her last child, Zeus, was born, she hurried to hide him on a Cretan mountain – Ida. She gave Kronos a stone to swallow instead.

"He's gone senile, let him suffer. Let him eat the boulder, and let it get stuck in his stomach!"

Meanwhile, the newly-born child was not having a bad time at all. Don't even mention abandoned children. No way! Whatever else went on in the mountains, he grew up a true prince with the help of the Nymphs, Amaltheia, and the Kuretes. When he became an adult he went straight to his father, dethroned him and forced him to …vomit up his other children. He then shared out the kingdom with his brothers as follows: he himself became the lord of the universe, Poseidon lord of the seas and Hades lord of the underworld. Then, just as his father had done, he decided to marry his sister – Hera – and start a family.

And that was it. The first 'divine' families began to produce children and like wildfire the world was filled with gods, demigods and heroes. The first and best lived on Olympos, the highest mountain peak of Greece, in gilded palaces. They enjoyed life and had a great time eating delicious bread – ambrosia – and drinking sweet wine, the famous nectar.

Battles of the Titans and the Giants

Zeus huffed and puffed. "Swallow one's own children? Is that the act of a father?"

These thoughts went through his mind and his anger at Kronos blew up and bubbled over. He could stand it no longer. He called together his brothers and sisters and spoke to them. "We'll take revenge on him and all of his kind. War on the Titans!"

That's what he said, and that's what happened. The young people believed that they would deal quickly with their old uncles, and that would be that. However, ten whole years passed and the score in the Gods v. Titans game was 0-0. In the last minute of time, Earth advised Zeus to bring in his uncles, the Cyclopes and the Hundred Armed Ones who had been unjustly treated and were still imprisoned in the depths of the Earth, on his side. Happy and grateful, the Cyclopes gave Zeus thunder and lightning. The Hundred Armed Ones, for their part, lifted up huge rocks with great ease and crushed the Titans. Being struck by rocks on the one hand and thunder and lightning on the other, the Titans were finally beaten and tossed down into Tartaros.

The Gods were not able to relax before problems started with the Giants. These man-like beings, which resembled twin snakes from the midriff downwards, launched a furious attack on the Gods. They certainly had the support of Earth, who this time fought against her grandchildren. The monsters with the snakes in their beards and hair began to toss rocks and tree trunks furiously at the Olympians. Things were looking difficult. The only hope for all was …a miraculous herb. Zeus forbade Helios (the sun), Selene (the moon) and Eos (the dawn) from appearing, in order to make it difficult for his opponents to look for the herb in the dark. As soon as he had found it himself, the opponents began to fall upon each other.

Granny Earth could not bear the defeat and thought that the time had come for Zeus to receive a hard lesson…so she herself gave birth to a fearsome monster, Typhon. Want us to describe him? From the waist upwards he was a man, from the midriff downwards he was a dragon, the heads of snakes sprang from his shoulders, fire came from his jaws and he was so big, that he touched the sky and when he opened his arms one reached to the east and the other to the west. Pure, total terror! The gods took fright, changed themselves into animals and hid in Egypt - apart from Zeus, brave guy, who stayed to face him. In the end, he not only defeated him but managed to toss all of Etna on top of him, and squash him flat!

ZEUS

Zeus escaped the madness of his father, grew up on Cretan Ida and went back to take his revenge. We've already said that. Now, he sat well on his throne, a victor. He was lord of the world, the controller of the weather and the father not only of men but also of most of the gods, demigods and heroes! How did that come about? Well, it doesn't take a lot of thinking about. If you have so much power and are two metres tall, the girls adore you! And what if he was married to Hera? He couldn't care less. Zeus found a way to get to them…so he filled the world with children, ensuring the perpetuation of his line but also an increase in the population of the earth.

With his official wife he had four children – Hephaestos, Ares, Hebe and Eileithyia. Huh, they were not the best!

"Do kids take after the mother who bore them?" He spoke with gritted teeth. "I'll try with some other women," he thought, so as to prove it. In fact he began with almost any woman he saw, goddess, mortal, beautiful, plain, filling the world with children. And the truth of the matter is that some of these were real gems!

Look, with Metis, the daughter of Okeanos, he produced Athena, goddess of wisdom. With the Titan daughter Leto he produced Apollo and Artemis, and with Maia, daughter of Atlanta, he produced Hermes. Demeter bore him Persephone and Semele bore him Dionysos, god of wine. With Themis he produced the Hours and Fates, with Mnemosyne the Nine Muses, and with Eurynome the Three Graces.

When he took it into his head to disguise himself, his couplings were spectacular. Really overdone! Don't imagine anything simple, such as 'I'll change my clothes and make-up and I'll look like my neighbour…' Nothing like that. Disguised as a bull, he tricked the princess Europa and with her produced Minos, Rhadamanthos and Sarpedon. As a shower of gold he entered the bedroom of Danäe at Argos, slept with her and then Perseus was born. Changing another time into a beautiful swan, he approached Leda who impulsively hugged him - and then Beautiful Helen was born.

These are only a few of the saucy stories about Zeus and beautiful girls. We don't need to say how furious Hera became and how much nastiness resulted from her jealousy…

HERA

Hera, one of the three daughters of Kronos and Rhea and a serious girl by nature, loved to go on solitary walks in the countryside. One day when she was strolling on the mountain it suddenly started to rain. Just as she was about to go, a cuckoo, soaked and in a bad state, fell in front of her feet.

"Poor little thing, come here and let me warm you," she said, and took the little bird in her arms. How was the innocent girl to know!

All of a sudden, the cuckoo took on the form of Zeus. That crafty individual had changed form to trick her and make her his wife. At length, the two were married and had four children – Hephaestos, Ares, Hebe and Eileithyia. Her children were not such as you would admire, but then she herself was not the best mum in the world…as soon as she saw how ugly Hephaestos was she threw him into the sea. Ah well!

As the 'first lady' of Olympos - because she had married the king of the gods - she was considered the protectoress of marriage and the family. How ironic! They call you the protectoress of the family, and you can't even save your own! You see, her husband was very lively and constantly chasing other women, divine or mortal. She herself was terribly jealous, but she could do nothing about Zeus. So, she worked off steam by pursuing her rivals and their children. The list of her intrigues is endless, so for that reason we will only describe the more fascinating ones.

She made it difficult for Leto to produce Zeus' children by forcing her to move from place to place when she was about to give birth. She changed Io into a cow and sent a fly to bother her. She changed Kallisto, who produced Arkas together with Zeus, into a bear and sent Artemis to kill her. She was indescribably harsh with Semele, Dionysos' mother, making her catch fire from the very brilliance of Zeus. Her hatred for Herakles, Zeus' son, was so great that she persecuted him from the moment of his birth by sending snakes into his cradle. It didn't stop there, either. When he grew up, it was Hera who made him a slave of Eurystheus, king of Mycenae…

Her jealousy was so great that at some point she actually believed that she could take on Zeus himself. So, in the more important wars, such as the one with the Titans, the one with the Giants and the Trojan War, she fought along with the opposing camp, undermining her own husband!

ATHENA

When Zeus was very young - perhaps it was before he married Hera - he met one of the daughters of Okeanos one day and was impressed by her. He went right away to Earth, her grandmother, and said "I want to marry her."

"Out of the question!" shrieked she. "Metis is the cleverest woman in the universe. If she has a son, he will take your throne."

Zeus, who was mad - in fact crazy - about the young girl, had already slept with her. She was pregnant and now the all-powerful god was beside himself.

"What shall I do?"

He paced up and down but found no solution. In his desperation, he opened his mouth one minute and swallowed her at a gulp. "There," he said. "That's the best solution. I have not only taken all the wisdom and knowledge of Metis inside me and made it mine, but also the dangerous child that she was carrying."

Not much time had passed, certainly less than nine months, when Zeus began to suffer from a terrible headache. Neither Hera with her medical knowledge nor the goddesses with their herbs could help him. As the pressure in his head increased, Zeus nearly went mad. So he goes to Hephaestos and says "I need a strong axe. Throw me one."

The young man hummed and hawed, but did what his father had asked. When he opened up his head with it, the fully armed Athena sprang out. She was the child whom Metis had been carrying, and now the time had come for her – in this strange way - to enter the world! Armed and pure, unmarried and wise - exactly as she had been at her birth - she was to remain all her life. These gifts helped her to defeat her uncle, tough Poseidon, in the contest to find out who would be the protector of Athens. He offered water, she the olive tree. And she won! This is why the city was called Athens and on its highest point, the Acropolis, a magnificent temple was built, dedicated to the maiden, the unmarried goddess, and called the Parthenon.

Athena should not at all be thought of as a goddess of war. Even though she was armed, she had nothing to do with Ares, the bringer of war. Her aim was not physical domination, but the victory of logic, method and strategy. Besides being sharp-witted in war she was also sharp as a needle in peacetime. A real lady, she loved literature and the fine arts such as sculpture and painting. Not to mention that she loved things to do with housekeeping! As an excellent housewife she taught women how to use the weaving loom, and as a true lover of the arts she invented an important musical instrument – the flute.

POSEIDON

If you have a brother like Zeus, well of course you're going to be someone important yourself. So Poseidon was named – without sitting any exams – lord of the sea! His weapon was the trident and his home a mythical palace on the seabed. He enjoyed life and his regal position there, along with his wife, the Nereid Amphitrite, whom he loved dearly. The two of them had a son, Triton, a happy little sprite who was half-man and half-fish. Thanks to this strange little being, the sea was filled with enchanting sounds which issued when he blew into seashells. When Triton tired of making music, he looked after the golden chariot and the superb white horses of his father. He was such a good kid that one day Poseidon gave him a hippocamp to play with. This cute little animal was half-horse and half-fish, so in a way it looked a little like Triton!

Tough, imposing and sour-tempered, Poseidon got cross from time to time and whipped up the sea, putting boats and people in danger. When the waters calmed down again, everyone knew that the king had relaxed and was quiet again. Of course, this was a rare occurrence, because being so nervy he was always at odds with someone. Sometimes with his sister Hera, sometimes with his niece Athena, or with anyone else who crossed his path.

They even said that when he was beaten by Athena over the naming of the city, he got so angry that the sea swelled up and almost drowned Athens!

From time to time he got bored with stirring up the waters and went on a trip into the 'outside world'. There, just like Zeus, he was very fond of chasing beautiful girls. When he was still a boy and growing up on Rhodes under the watchful eye of the Telchines, he was much in love with Alia, their sister. With her, he produced six sons and one daughter, the very beautiful Rhodos, who gave her name to the island. Later on he married Amphitrite, who was then his official wife. Even if she was a nymph and a real dolly as well, Poseidon cheated her many times. He of course had many children, some of whom were quite…in a class of their own. The Cyclopes and the horses were just some of his strange offspring. Amongst the horses was winged Pegasos, who sprang from the head of the Medusa, and the horse named Areion which Demeter bore him, then there were the giants Otos, Ephialtes and Tityos, the Cyclopes Polyphemos and the fearsome bandit Prokrustes. It was even said by some that Theseus was his son, although most believed he was the son of Aegeus, king of Athens.

DEMETER

Dignified and of sturdy build, Demeter waved her finger at her sisters and said "You stay in and take care of the house and the family. I'll look after the fields."

"Brr, but it's cold," said Hestia and got near to the fire.

"Tut, tut, that's men's work," squeaked Hera and continued her magic which was aimed at punishing some of Zeus' girlfriends.

Demeter, however, did what she said. She blessed the earth and it bore fruit. Men had food to eat, they could feed their children, and they were happy. "That's a fine woman," they said, and worshipped her in temples and sanctuaries.

One day, when Demeter was tired of travelling the earth from one end to the other and keeping an eye on the fields, she called a young man, Triptolemos, and told him "I'll teach you the secrets of cultivation, but you must undertake to pass them on to all Mankind."

"OK," he answered, liking the idea that he would be the first farmer on the planet! So people learned to plough, sow, thresh and reap. It was a feast for Demeter's eyes!

Zeus saw her unwinding, and thought "Snooty! Now I'll take care of her."

So he changed into a bull and got close to her.

The goddess was taken in and after a short while she gave birth to a little girl, the beautiful Persephone.

Because Demeter was herself very prudish and straight-laced, her girl turned out well. Otherwise she would have had no chance to get married and become a mother. Demeter adored her daughter and the two of them became inseparable. As the seasons changed, the clean air and the sun brought even more of a glow to Persephone's cheeks. Pluto saw her and became crazy about her.

"I'll kidnap her and make her queen of the Underworld," he said to himself. So one day, when Persephone was playing with the daughters of Okeanos, a narcissus sprang up before her.

"How beautiful!" she said, and bent to pick it. Then the earth opened, Pluto came out in his golden chariot, snatched the girl and took her down to his realm. She called out for help and was heard by Hecate and Helios, who immediately told Demeter. The unhappy mother began to roam the seas and the land to find her precious girl. In vain, however! In her despair she abandoned the earth, which in that year did not bring about any germination at all. Everything shrivelled up – flowers, trees, plants. People started to be alarmed and make noises. So did

HERMES

The son of Zeus and Maia was born at green Kyllene in the Peloponnese, inside a cave. Clever, quick, crafty but for the most part a thief and rogue, from the hour of his birth he was busy with jokes and playing tricks. He was barely a few hours old when he decided to get up and leave his cradle. Who would have expected him to manage to walk and leave the cave! While he was strolling about and getting to know the world, he came upon a tortoise and was fascinated. It was not only its shape, colour and the slow way it moved, but mainly the strange, hard, curved shell which it carried on its back. As soon as he saw this, a great idea took root in his brain and without losing a moment, he killed the tortoise. He took the precious shell and stretched seven strings, made from animal gut, across it. That was it – the first lyre in the world became a reality! Enthusiastic, the little chap sat in a corner and entertained himself with the melodic sounds from his creation. Several hours passed in this way, until he suddenly began to feel hungry. For milk, that is - not for a chat.

"I'll have to eat something to give me strength," he mused. "Shall I go and steal my brother Apollo's cattle? Wouldn't that be a joke?"

In a flash he goes to Pieria and makes off with fifty cows from the divine herd. He brings them to the Peloponnese, kills two of them, roasts them and eats them in no time at all. Happy, and above all full, he returned to the cave and lay down like… a good baby in his cradle. Next day, in the morning, Apollo arrived in a fury. "Where are my cattle?"

"Which cattle?" asked the baby, apparently without interest.

"I'll deal with you myself," said big brother. Quick as a flash he took up the little one and brought him to Zeus. The father of the two boys split his sides laughing at the craftiness of the baby, and advised them to make it up. On the way home Hermes, to humour Apollo, began to play his lyre. Apollo was enchanted by the sound of the new instrument. "I'll give it to you as a gift," said the trickster, provided you give me something in return. "Whatever you want," said Apollo.

"I want the cattle, the golden wand (caduceus) of success and wealth, and the skill of prophecy."

The little 'businessman' asked for a lot and he got it, except for the skill of prophecy which Apollo kept for himself. He allowed him, however, to predict the way that dice would fall; so it was that besides becoming the 'lord' of commerce, he became lord of gambling, too. He also operated the gods' postal service. Zeus gave him the ability to travel quickly and take messages, wearing winged sandals and a special cap.

ARES

In contrast to sly Hermes, whom the Greeks liked a lot, everyone detested Ares. They were right. How can you love someone who behaves like a storm, spreading catastrophe? For this reason he was the 'Lord of War', the personification of destruction.

The only son of that most illustrious couple, Zeus and Hera, he showed his rotten character from an early age. Badly brought up as he was, he circulated provocatively in his golden helmet and with shining weapons, quarrelling with everyone. He even squabbled with his sister Athena, the wise goddess, who planned every movement she made in war with care. By contrast, Ares was so much of a maniac that he was only interested in hullabaloo and destruction. What did he care who was to blame or not to blame? Here, he fooled his mother Hera, when she asked him to help the Greeks in the Trojan War.

"Of course, mum," he said. Next day, he fought…on the Trojan side.

This savage had a daughter, Alcippe, granddaughter of Cecrops, king of Athens. When one day Allirothios, the son of Poseidon, dared to touch her, Ares killed him without a further thought. However, he didn't get off lightly. The other gods made him sit down on a rock and judged him severely. This rock is still called the Areopagos today – the name means 'Ares' rock'.

Apart from Alcippe, Ares produced many more children with various women. It was his magnificence and strength which charmed them.

He produced Harmony with Aphrodite, the goddess of beauty who was very wily. Her official husband Hephaestos was not enough for her; she wanted adventures with her own brother! However, since a god loves not only the thief but also the master, one morning Helios - who sees everything - went and revealed to Hephaestos what was happening behind his back. Hephaestos was very bitter about the whole thing and applied all his intelligence and skill to the construction of an invisible net. When the illicit pair went to bed they were caught in the net, like a mouse in a trap which doesn't know what lies in store for it…

All the gods gathered together, laughed and humiliated them so much that Aphrodite was forced to flee away to Cyprus, and wiseguy Ares to his homeland of Thrace. However, the two of them did manage to produce some children, amongst them Eros, Deimos and Phobos.

APHRODITE

Aphrodite took her name from the sea foam, because she was born in it. Swimming off, she reached Cyprus and for that reason many people called her the Cyprian.

Dolly and hag that she was, women hated her, while all the men wanted to marry her. Wherever she set foot on Olympos she caused a great stir. The gods, first and foremost Zeus, were open-mouthed at her beauty. The goddesses, on the other hand, were upset. "She has no brains in her head," said wise Athena.

"She seduces men and breaks up homes," wailed Hestia, the goddess of the family.

"The only things she has in her mind are love affairs," complained virgin Artemis.

The gifts and countless proposals of marriage were such that this very beautiful goddess was bound to marry someone her equal. It was a great surprise to everyone when her marriage to lame Hephaestos was announced. But Aphrodite never considered him to be enough for her. Ares, Anchises, Adonis, Poseidon and Dionysos are only a few of the men her eye fell upon and whom she seduced. With some of them, certainly, she produced children, such as with the god of war. As we have already said, that relationship did not have a happy end. Deimos, Phobos, Eros and Harmony were their four children. The first two, who were the personification of terror, looked like their father, and the other two took after their mother.

Apart from being a wolf of a woman, Aphrodite was also a trickster, because she was very fond of making gods get involved with mortals. Zeus, since this kind of foolery was not at all to his taste, decided to take revenge on her. He made her fall in love with Anchises, a very good-looking, well-built shepherd. With him, she produced a very handsome and charismatic little boy, Aeneas, who later became king of Troy.

Even Poseidon, god of the sea, fell into her web. He loved her very much and with her produced a son, Erykas, who later became king of far-off Sicily.

Our girl Aphrodite, whose life was ridden with scandals, sometimes became serious beyond recognition. Like when she fell in love with that very handsome youth, Adonis. Her love for him was so great that when he was killed while hunting, she wept inconsolably and from her tears anemones sprang up!

HEPHAESTOS

So what if you are the son of Zeus, so what if you haven't a literary bent - well then, you become a craftsman. Certainly, Hephaestos was not just anyone, he was the best smith on Olympos and in the whole world. No matter what he set his eyes on, his hands were always busy with something. He may have been ugly, but his talent and intelligence more than made up for it! Speaking of his ugliness, they said that a worse-looking baby had never been born. Even his own mother – Hera - took fright as soon as she saw him and threw him into the sea to get rid of him. By his good luck, after sinking for nine days, he fell into the arms of the Nereid Thetis who undertook to raise him in secret, in a cave. The poor kid stayed for nine years in the depths of the sea and having nothing else to do, immersed himself in metalworking. Now a young man, but still terribly ugly, tall, fat and lame, he decided to go to Olympos and find justice. When his mother saw him, she pretended to be moved.

"My little boy, at last you've come back!"

"I've not only come back, I've bought you a present."

"What a lovely chair!" The heartless mother ran to sit down on what her son had created. Then she tried to stand up again, but it was impossible. The crafty son, to get his revenge on her for having thrown him into the sea, had added some invisible straps and she was held fast. Nobody heard her and came to free her, and only when Dionysos arrived was a solution found. The god of wine offered the young man a glass and he, ignorant as he was, immediately got drunk.

"I'll release her, but only if you give me Aphrodite for a wife." That's what he said, and that's what happened. The ugliest god married the most beautiful. What did he expect? Aphrodite turned out to be…lively, and was never slow to deceive him. When Hephaestos learned that she was having fun with his brother Ares, he sat down to make an invisible net. As soon as the illicit pair went to lie down in bed, they were caught and became the laughing stock of all Olympos!

So clever and skilled with his hands was Hephaestos. That was only a small sample of his wonderful work. They said that even the palaces of the gods on Olympos were his creations, as well as the bed of Helios, the darts of Artemis and Apollo, Agamemnon's sceptre and the bronze giant Talos. The list doesn't stop there. This supreme craftsman made the arms and shields of

the two greatest heroes, Herakles and Achilles.

Most important of all, they said that even Pandora, his first wife, was his own creation! He had fashioned her from earth and water, made her beautiful and tough, and given her a voice, following the instructions of Zeus.

DIONYSOS

Zeus noticed the daughter of king Kadmos one day and was inflamed by her beauty.

"I want to make you my wife," he said to the girl and she, knowing nothing of the world, believed him. Hera was not slow in realizing her husband's strategy and when Semele became pregnant, she was immediately beside herself.

"I'll get my revenge," she thought and began to weave her…spells. With one of them she changed form and appeared to the girl.

"My dear young woman, if it is really true that Zeus loves you, why have you never seen him, in his majesty and prime, when he moves around on Olympos?"

"Maybe he's trying to fool me," thought Semele and immediately demanded…an official appearance by her husband. Zeus knew well what would happen, but it was too late for him to back down. He appeared therefore as a real king, with regal splendour and full of majesty. Poor little Semele didn't have time to marvel at him before she was set ablaze by his radiance. She was totally consumed by the fire, and Zeus only just managed to save the child she was carrying in her belly. Semele was lost, and Hera rejoiced. The baby, since it was still very small and the time for its birth had not come, was kept for a short while by its father in a strange way,

beneath the skin of his leg. Yes he put it in there, like into a belly, and left it to grow! As soon as nine months had passed, the baby was born…for the second time. That is why they called it the 'twice-born'. What does Zeus do – he gives the baby to Hermes for him to hide well, so as to escape the anger of Hera. Hermes gave it to Ino, Semele's sister. But Hera, who had seen all that went on, made Ino and her

Maenads, Satyrs and Silenes. The grapes and the sweet wine which the young man discovered were shared with his friends, and with lunatic high spirits they ran around, danced and sang all day. There was no reason for him to abandon his happy way of life and move to Olympos, quite apart from the fact that he was afraid of Hera…

That witch never stopped her pursuit of him. Even now that he had grown up she set out to drive him mad. The poor devil started wandering the globe without reason or aim. Luckily he knew about vineyards, so his journeys were not a waste of time. They said that he taught the art of making wine even as far away as India!

Vineyards on the one hand and parties, high spirits and fun on the other, people adored Dionysos and his friends. To please them, he organized festivals at every opportunity. Festivals for the coming of spring, the flowering of Nature, the opening of the wine barrels…from these rituals theatre was born, for the first time in the world!

However, having a good time was not enough for Dionysos. He also wanted the security of married life. So he chose Ariadne, the daughter of Minos, and made her his companion. They said of course that the princess had fled with her fiancé Theseus from Crete, but when they arrived on Naxos the god ordered the hero to leave the girl behind, so that he could marry her himself.

husband go mad and set them to kill their children. Zeus hurried again to save Dionysos. He changed him into a little goat and sent him with Hermes to Mount Nysa, for the Nymphs to bring him up.

Dionysos had a good time out in the country, in the company of a load of exotic beings such as the

EROS

If you're a naked, mischievous kid, they say you're charming! If you're chubby and have wings they call you an angel. However, they don't call you a god. And yet for the ancient Greeks this mischievous child was a god, and actually one of the most loved. His wings, which were golden, were worn to separate him from the ordinary children in the neighbourhood who went about playing with bows and arrows. For this chubby, fifteen-year-old did not aim at…birds, but at gods and men, and he aimed straight for the heart. Not to kill them, but to arouse them. To make them fall in love.

You see, he was the son of Aphrodite and Ares. He was endowed from both sides so as to make his mark on men, for better or worse…

However, because cleverness catches itself out, one day when the young man was messing around, lying on the grass, his arrow turned back upon him and he was wounded himself. He fell very much in love with a beautiful princess called Psyche!

"How did I get into this trouble? Mum will be furious!"

What can you expect! Aphrodite became so jealous of the girl's beauty that she wanted only to do her harm. What does Eros do? He calls Zephyros and tells him "For this and that reason…I can't reveal myself at all. But I love her. So bring her to my palace for me. After that, I'll see what I can do."

"Your wish is my command," said Zephyros and ran like the wind. He brought the fantastically beautiful girl and set her down in the lap of luxury. Dazzled by the wealth, the girl melted at the tenderness of Eros. She felt truly happy. What did it matter that he was invisible? They agreed to live together in this way forever. She wouldn't be able to see him, but she would hear him and feel him.

However, since love affairs never last for long, the grumbling soon started.

"I only ask one favour of you, let my sisters come and see me," she pleaded and her nagging tore at Eros' heart. He gave in. That got him into trouble, because the sisters came and when they saw the splendour there they were bursting with envy.

"He must have a reason to hide himself from you. He might be a snake, a dragon or some fearsome monster," they told her. The poor kid was terrified and took it into her mind to kill him. As soon as night fell, she approached him with a lamp. What monster? Her husband was fantastic-looking, a true god! But the mistake had been made. Eros vanished instantly, exactly as they had agreed. Now unhappy Psyche began to roam the deserts in the hope of finding him somewhere…

She wandered, suffered, and appealed in her